On the Beach

Marilyn Woolley

As I walked along the beach,
I found this feather.

It belonged to a seagull
that lived by the sea.

As I walked along the beach,
I found this shell.

It belonged to a mussel
that lived in the sea.

As I walked along the beach,
I found this claw.

It belonged to a crab
that lived in the sea.

As I walked along the beach,
I found this shell with a hole on the top.

It belonged to a sea urchin
that lived in the sea.

As I walked along the beach,
I found this bone.

It belonged to a cuttlefish
that lived in the sea.

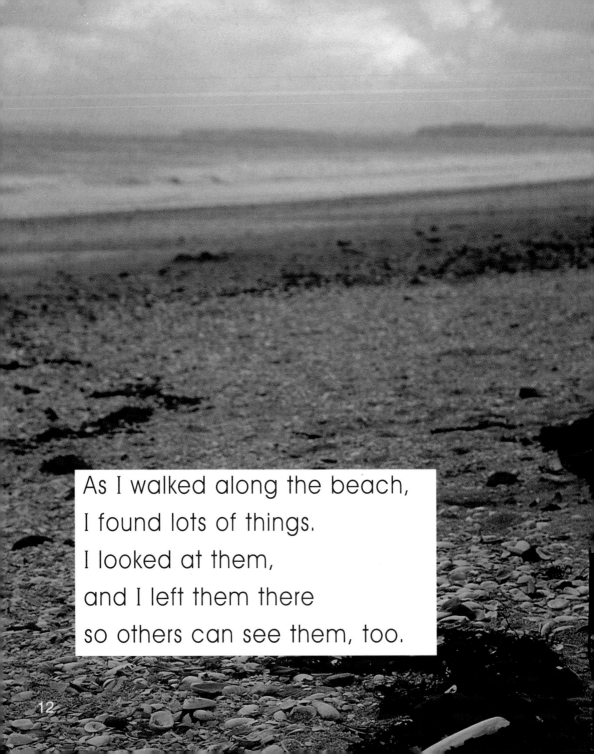

As I walked along the beach,
I found lots of things.
I looked at them,
and I left them there
so others can see them, too.